One Meal More
A Multicultural Ramadan Story

by Emma Apple

Published by Little Moon Books

First Edition
Paperback

ISBN-13: 978-0-473-47925-1

littlemoonbooks.com

One Meal More

A Multicultural Ramadan Story

On a **Ramadan** evening,
the table was set, **one** plate of
samboosas, awaiting the guests.

Then it began,
with a knock at the door...

An **Australian** guest,
with one meal more.

"Pavlova, for dessert!"
she said.

And there were **two** meals now.

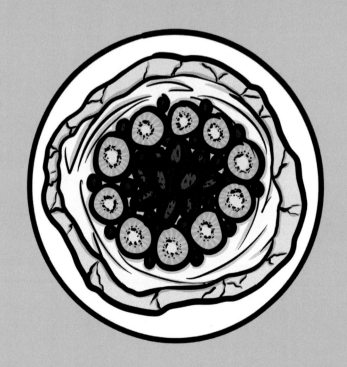

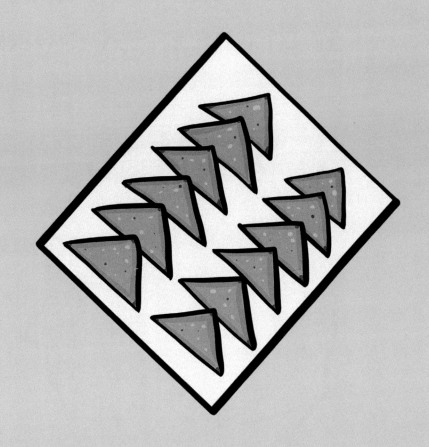

Later that evening,
a knock at the door...

A **Japanese** guest,
with one meal more.

"Fresh **sushi**"
she said.

And there were **three** meals now.

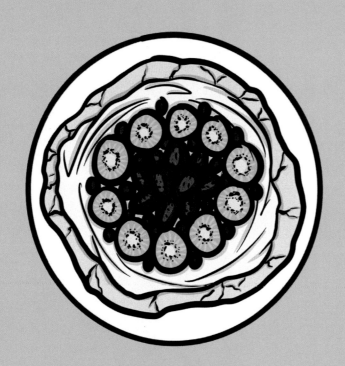

Later that evening,
a knock at the door...

13

A **Pakistani** guest,
with one meal more.

"A pot of **biryani!**"
she said.

And there were **four** meals now.

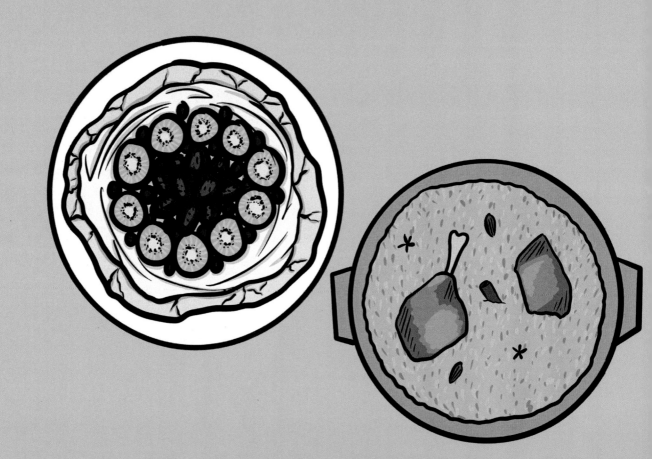

Later that evening,
a knock at the door...

An **Ethiopian** guest,
with one meal more.

"**Coffee** for all!"
she said.

And there were **five** meals now.

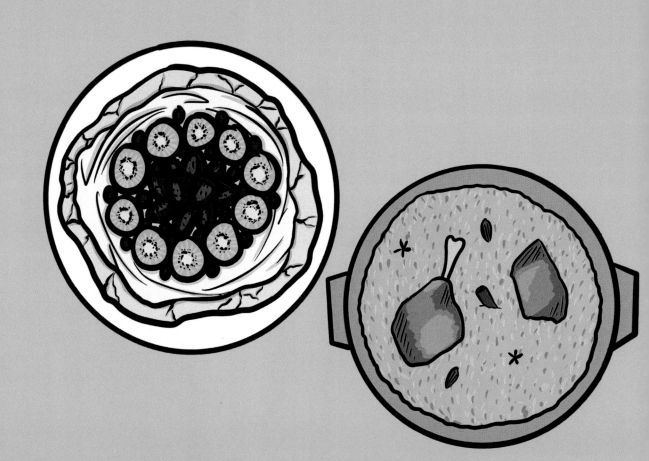

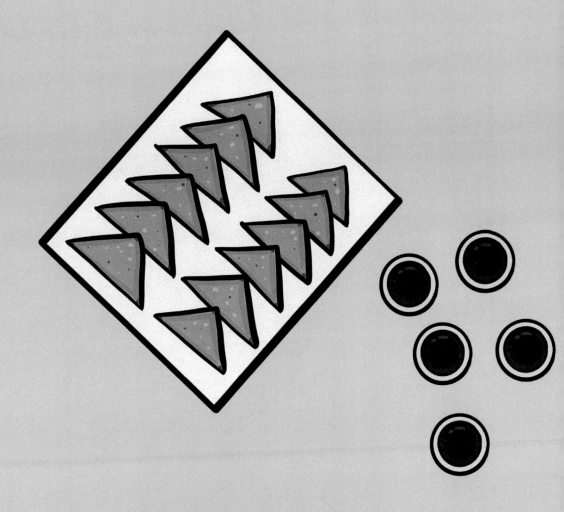

Later that evening,
a knock at the door...

A **Greek** guest,
with one meal more.

"A plate of **moussaka**."
she said.

And there were **six** meals now.

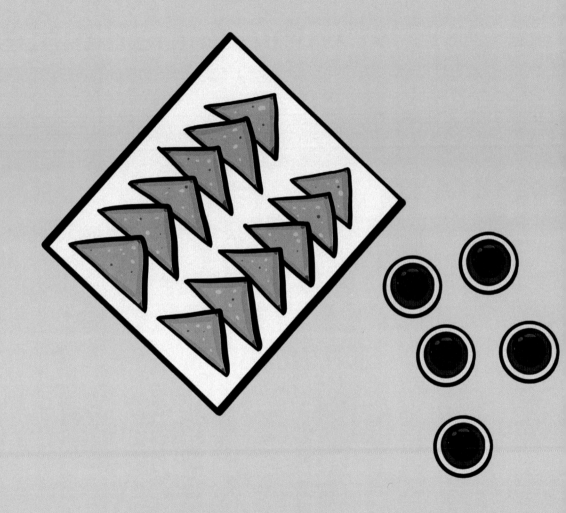

Later that evening,
a knock at the door...

A **Finnish** guest,
with one meal more.

"Some **karelian pies?**"
she said.

And there were **seven** meals now.

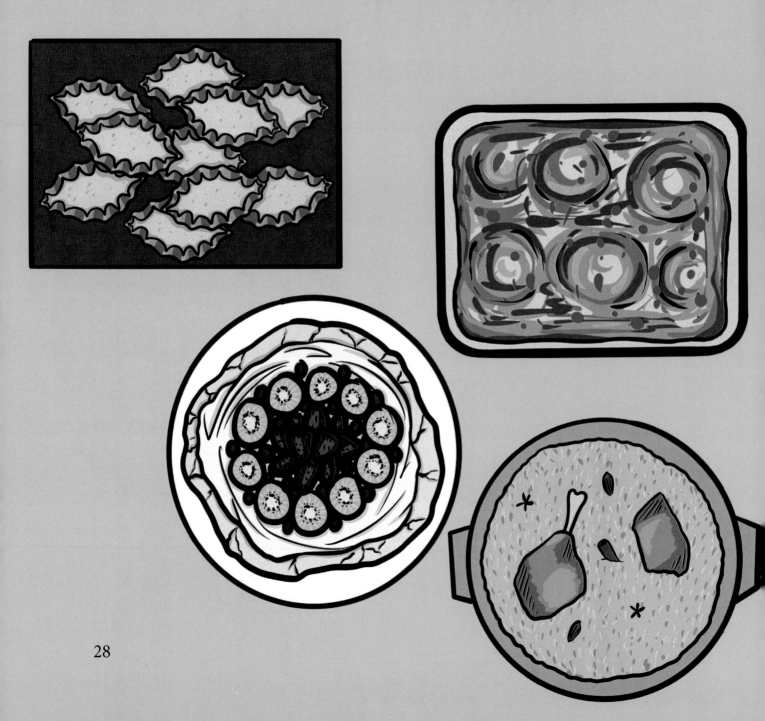

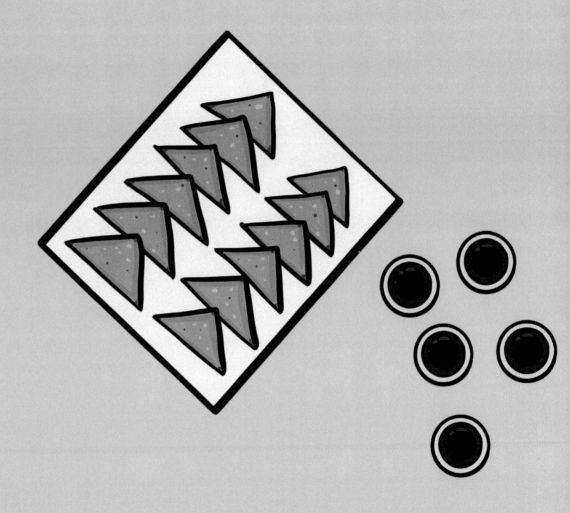

Later that evening,
a knock at the door...

A **French** guest,
with one meal more.

"I've brought **baguettes**."
she said.

And there were **eight** meals now.

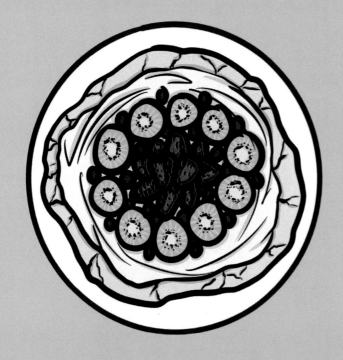

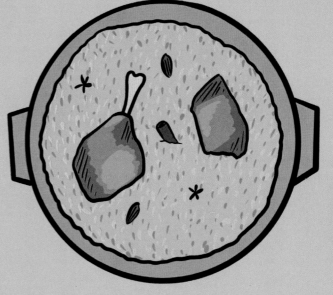

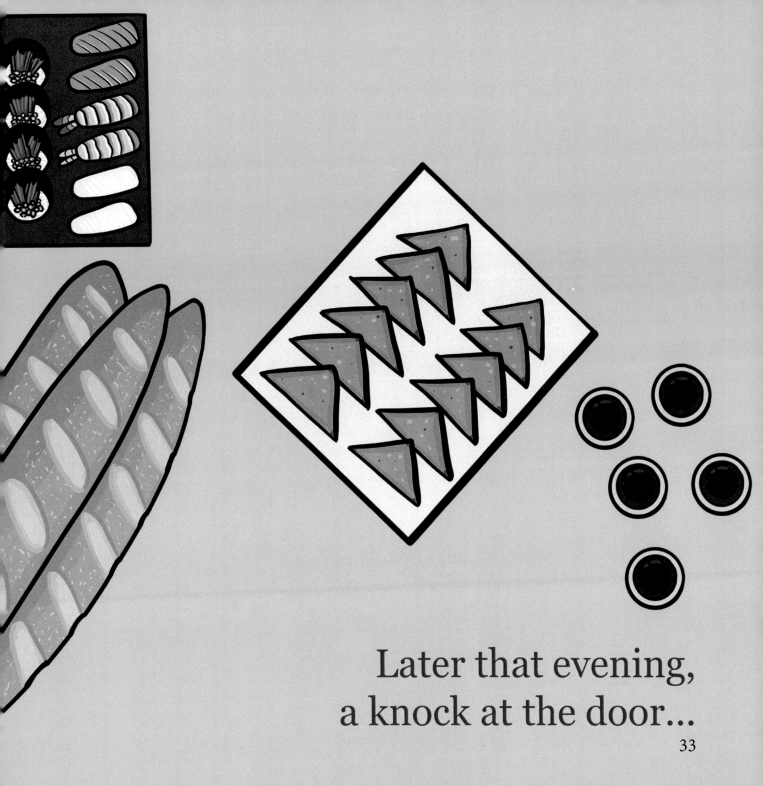

Later that evening,
a knock at the door...

An **American** guest,
with one meal more.

"Warm **apple pie**."
she said.

And there were **nine** meals now.

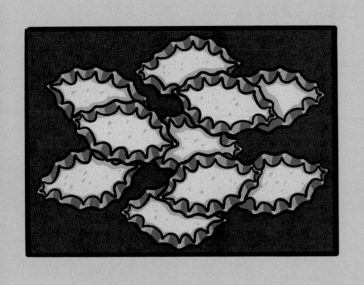

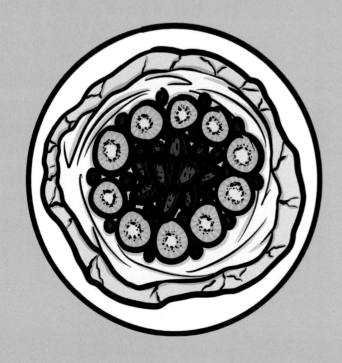

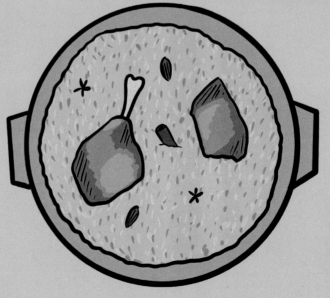

Later that evening,
a knock at the door...

A **Mexican** guest,
with one meal more.

"Delicious **guacamole**."
she said.

And there were **ten** meals now.

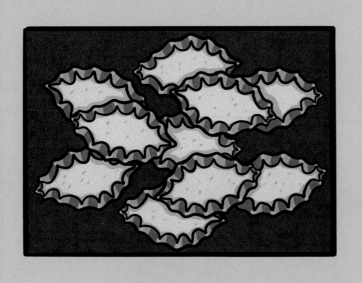

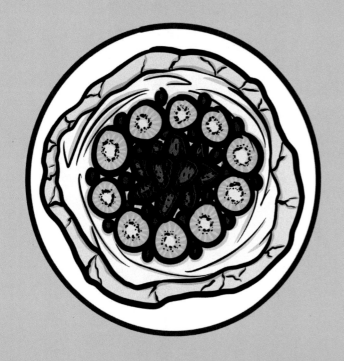

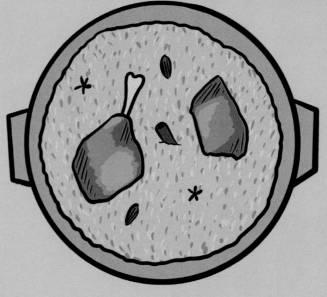

The sky was golden,
the sun had set,
the call to prayer began.

Clank went the plates.
Click went the spoons.
Clink went the glasses
of water.

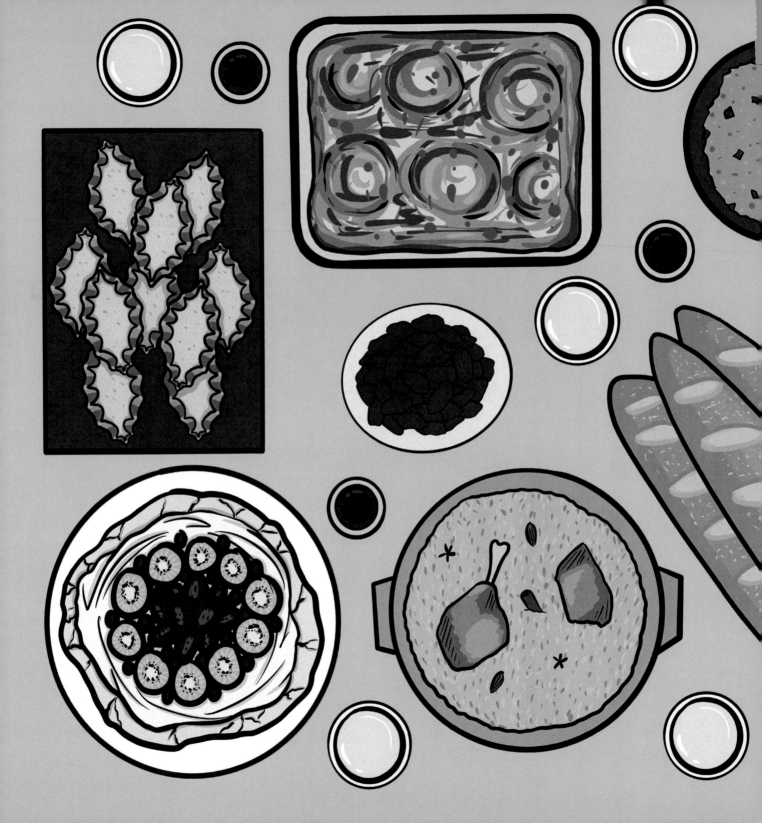

"Bismillah, please have a date!"

So they all sat down, and together they ate.

The meals on the map

MORE BOOKS FROM LITTLE MOON BOOKS

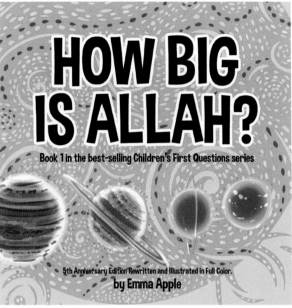

LITTLE
MOON
BOOKS

littlemoonbooks.com

Made in the USA
Las Vegas, NV
25 April 2021